Dedicated to my son Thomas Robert Glenn

Avago Aardvark went
on a trip with school,

Sean Glenn
Illustrations by Andy Burgess

Avago the Aardvark goes Swimming

Bumblebee Books
London

BUMBLEBEE PAPERBACK EDITION

Copyright © Sean Glenn 2021
Illustrations by Andy Burgess

The right of Sean Glenn to be identified as author of
this work has been asserted in accordance with sections 77 and 78 of the Copyright, Designs and Patents Act 1988.

All Rights Reserved

No reproduction, copy or transmission of this publication
may be made without written permission.
No paragraph of this publication may be reproduced,
copied or transmitted save with the written permission of the publisher, or in accordance with the provisions
of the Copyright Act 1956 (as amended).

Any person who commits any unauthorised act in relation to
this publication may be liable to criminal
prosecution and civil claims for damage.

A CIP catalogue record for this title is
available from the British Library.

ISBN: 978-1-83934-078-9

Bumblebee Books is an imprint of
Olympia Publishers.

First Published in 2021

Bumblebee Books
Tallis House
2 Tallis Street
London
EC4Y 0AB

Printed in Great Britain

www.olympiapublishers.com

He and his friends
were off to the pool.

Avago's classmates
just rushed right in

But Avago worried that
he just couldn’t swim.

As soon as the water
touched Avago's toes

He trembled, he shook,
his body just froze.

Have a go Avago!
It's so much fun,

But Avago yearned
just to play in the sun.

He watched as his friends were jumping and splashing

And with a hop and a bounce
Hetty Hippo came crashing.

The wave covered Avago
from his toes to his snout.

"I'm all wet, I'm all wet,"
he crossly cried out.

Standing there soaked
he began to laugh,

"Jump in, jump in,"
cried Gerry Giraffe.

Avago knew it was
time to be brave,

To play with his friends
was all that he craved.

Ever so slowly he
stepped in the pool,

And learning to swim
was surprisingly cool.

The whole of his class let out such a big cheer,

Avago jumped and he
splashed with nothing to fear.

You see sometimes Avago
you just don't know,

The fun you'll be missing
till you just have a go.

About the Author

I’m a former nightclub owner that now owns a home removal company. I have a four year old son called Thomas who is my absolute world. Myself and Thomas love nothing more than trying out new activities together and making up stories along the way. Thomas is my inspiration to my writing.

I like to write in the hope my stories will promote kindness and encourage children to try new activities.